ISBN: 978-0-578-60523-4 (paperback)

Front cover and book's design by Stephen Minervino.

Printed by RTLD Publishing in the United State of America.

First printing edition 2019,

RTLD Publishing
2912 Falkirk Place
Raleigh, NC 27604

Facebook: @RiverTheThreeLeggedDog
Instagram: @RiverTheThreeLeggedDog

Dedications

To River. My heart and soul. You rescued me from my darkest days and for that I am eternally grateful.

~Caitlynne

To Mom and Dad. You've given me life in more ways than one. I love you.

~Stephanie

To my lovely wife, who always stands by my side. I will walk with you always.

~Stephen

My name is River,
and I'm a three-legged dog.

Being a three-legged dog is
just like being a four-legged dog.

It might take me a little longer to learn,

but I can do anything a four-legged dog can do.

I can swim!

I go on hikes in the woods.

I don't worry about how others may see me,

because I know I can do
whatever I put my mind to.

The end

The Authors

Stephanie Stegemoller was born in Miami Florida, but was raised in a small town in western North Carolina. She has a B.S. in Biology from Appalachian State University. In 2015, she moved to Raleigh where she studied as an actress. In 2016, she co-founded Dog-Eared Books. She still enjoys both acting and science, loves to read, sings her heart out anytime she's behind the wheel, and has a soft spot in her heart for animals. She currently lives in Raleigh, NC.

Caitlynne has harbored a lifelong love of books and animals. She was born and raised in Georgia and is an Appalachian State Alumni. She co-owns Dog-Eared Books, enjoys outdoor activities like hiking and kayaking, and most of all, still loves animals. She resides with her two dogs, River and Rory, and her 19-year-old cat, Tigger, in Raleigh, North Carolina.

The Artist

The Friends

Stephen Minervino was born in the south, raised in the north, and then made his way back down again to study Art and Design at NCSU. After graduating in 2014, he has worked as an animator and digital artist in the Raleigh area. While he has no pets of his own, he loves spending time with the pets of friends. Especially cats, even though they make his face explode. He loves a good story, whether it's a book, a video game, a movie, or a comic.

Handicapped. Crippled. Disabled. Broken. These are all words that have been used to describe River. None of them are true. He may be missing a leg, but he is an amazing addition to my little family. Many dogs and cats just like River are overlooked in shelters every day.

These animals may be old, missing a limb, blind, deaf, or be diagnosed with one disease or another. These "issues" do not make them less than "whole" animals.

If anything, it makes them more. They have persevered and just need one more chance to find that fur-ever home. The pets on the next two pages were all adopted by loving families who looked past their outward appearance and gave them another chance.

~Caitlynne

ODIN

Despite having an eye removed due to an unknown trauma before being adopted, Odin is quite the happy go lucky dog. His goal in life is to use silly antics to befriend everyone he meets.

PANCAKE

Pancake was found with an injury that required amputating his right front leg. He is a very happy kitty who loves to play, snuggle and head-boop, and he LOVES treats!

TED

Ted's left eye did not properly develop and he was born with sight in only one eye. But don't think for a single second that slows him down! Ted runs, plays, jumps over fallen trees, and chases every squirrel he sees with complete grace and glee.

BUDDY

Buddy may be missing a leg but don't tell him that; he still runs, jumps and plays will his 4-legged friends! Buddy is the best cuddler and loves his humans so much!

CPSIA information can be obtained
at www.ICGtesting.com
Printed in the USA
LVHW050203271119
638629LV00004B/5